The Cat Burglar
and
Other Stories
(A Moral Education Reader)

Dedicated to
Tamara, Robert, Timothy and Jonathan

THE CAT BURGLAR
AND
OTHER STORIES

(A MORAL EDUCATION READER)

Rosemary Pearson Chen

Graham Brash, Singapore

© Rosemary Pearson Chen, 1987

First published in 1987 by
Graham Brash (Pte) Ltd
36-C Prinsep Street
Singapore 0718

ISBN 9971-49-044-7

Cover and illustrations by Elaine Wee

Typeset by A-Z Graphic
Printed by General Printing & Publishing Services, S'pore

Introduction: The Sea of Life

Life is not always smooth sailing. Each boat sets forth with different equipment for this exciting adventure. Parents and teachers help equip us with knowledge to chart our journey into the future. They teach us to distinguish between right and wrong. They encourage us to do what we think is right.

As others influence us and help to make our vessels seaworthy, we struggle with conflicting desires. Often we are tempted to take the easy way, the most enjoyable route. It needs discipline and sacrifice to choose the upwind direction; to go against the current, to make waves standing up for the truth.

What is the 'right way'? Is it simply obeying the law, or does truth involve something more? Do we agree with abortion and capital punishment simply because they are legally accepted in Singapore? When faced with the responsibility of making decisions, what do we do?

These stories cover problems and challenges we will all face: criticism, ridicule, temptation, cruelty, disorganisation, selfishness, death, pain, depression, jealousy, suspicion, loneliness, disappointment, failure. How do we handle these situations? By pondering over these stories and relating the characters' reactions to your own life, I hope you will consider the moral problems and find solutions to some of your dilemmas.

Sometimes we may find our boat becalmed and not moving forward. These are times to trim the sails and prepare and plan for the next stage of the journey. Sometimes the wind of public opinion blows hard against us. Waves of ill fortune threaten to swamp and drown us. Visibility may be poor and we are fearful of the unknown. These are the times we seek shelter in a safe bay and drop anchor for refuge and rest. On other occasions we are strong and riding high. Then we should toss a towline to help weaker vessels struggling in deep waters.

6

We have compasses for direction and maps to guide our path. We ignore these at the risk of sailing into trouble. Accidents may happen, not always our fault, but we suffer the consequences. We can't make progress if we mope and blame the sea, or the weather, or our fellow vessels. We are each pilot of our own boat during this journey through life.

Happy sailing!

Rosemary Pearson Chen
1987

Contents

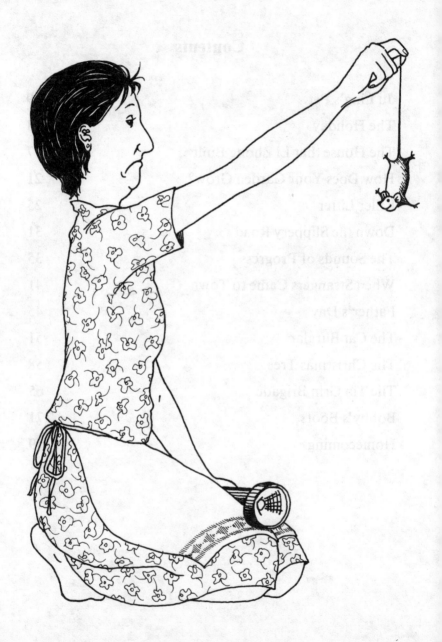

Ju Ling's Pet

Whiskers was a very small grey mouse who lived in a cage on the balcony of Block 127, #15-12. Ju Ling had brought her home from school for the holidays as there was nobody left at the school to care for the pets. Ju Ling's mother was terrified of mice. She didn't like the thought of having one in the house — even if it was securely locked in a cage.

But Ju Ling loved Whiskers. She fed her every day, cleaned her cage and made her exercise. She cut little windows in cardboard boxes and made rooms for the mouse to hide in. She tore up rags for nests and saved nuts and titbits of food for her pet. (Mrs Cai wondered why *she* bothered buying mouse traps and bait and pest sprays to keep her house free from rodents, while her daughter doted on one.)

One day when Ju Ling was out with her friends, Mrs Cai found the cage door open. "Oh no!" she gasped in horror, "Whatever's happened to Whiskers?" She was afraid of the little mouse and hated touching it, yet she knew her daughter would be very upset to lose Whiskers. Mother-love does strange things: Mrs Cai searched the entire flat. She looked in every cupboard and behind all the furniture. She shook the curtains and swept under the beds. She carefully opened boxes and moved all the flower-pots. She hunted high and low for the missing mouse. "Ju Ling will be so upset," thought Mrs Cai. "I must find Whiskers before she returns."

Eventually, she found the mouse. It was under the oven. When she flashed a torch, Mrs Cai saw two tiny eyes shining back at her. Without even thinking, she grabbed the long tail and, firmly holding it at arm's length, deposited the mouse in her cage. She promptly closed the door, then collapsed in a chair, shaking nervously.

Some time later, Ju Ling returned from the library and

carefully opened her bag. She took out a little box and carried it to the cage. Then she squealed with surprise. "Mum — now I have two mice! I took Whiskers to the library to show her to my friends and now another mouse is in the cage."

Mrs Cai laughed at Ju Ling's astonishment. "I thought Whiskers had escaped, so I tried to find her for you. I searched for ages."

Ju Ling looked hard at her mother. "But you hate mice, Mum."

"That's true," said Mrs Cai, "But you would have been very upset to lose your pet."

"Thanks, Mum," said Ju Ling, hugging her mother. "Susan asked me to find her a pet mouse. Can I give her your mouse?"

"By all means," said Mrs Cai, sighing with relief. "I don't fancy doubling our mouse population. Give it to Susan today."

A
1. What did Ju Ling and her mother think of mice?
2. Why did Mrs Cai look everywhere for the mouse?
3. How did she feel about having to pick up the mouse?
4. Why was Ju Ling so surprised when she came home from the library?
5. What adjectives can you think of to describe Mrs Cai's action?
6. How did Ju Ling react to her mother's kindness?

B
1. Have you ever done anything which you did not like in order to help someone?
2. What was the last kind deed you did for someone?
3. What is gratitude?
4. In what ways can a person express gratitude or appreciation? For example, how could Ju Ling have shown her gratitude to her mother?

C

1. Write an imaginary conversation between Ju Ling and her mother when Whiskers was first brought home from school.

2. Do you have a pet at home? Write an account of what you have to do to care for your pet properly.

3. Sometimes, through ignorance or thoughtlessness, owners can be cruel to their pets. Make up a story based on this theme.

The Holiday

Greg, Sharleen, Candy and James were very excited. They were going to Kuala Lumpur for a holiday, and as it is a very long journey by car, they planned to leave at 5 a.m. "It's the only way to avoid the traffic jam at the Causeway," said Dad. "It's cooler and more pleasant to travel before the mid-day heat," explained Mother. "We'll stop and have lunch and stretch our legs in Malacca to break the journey."

They spent all evening discussing details and packing. Mother tried to telephone her sister in Kuala Lumpur to tell her what time to expect them. She could not get through until after midnight when her sister returned home from a meeting. By that time everyone was tired and irritable from all the excitement. The children were squabbling about what games to take, as Dad had limited them to one game each to save space.

When the alarm rang at 4.30, no-one really felt like getting up or eating breakfast. It seemed like the middle of the night. When they were finally ready to leave, the children started arguing about who was to have the window seats. Mother intervened and said they could take turns; the two boys would sit in the middle as far as Malacca, then change places with the girls. They were only ten kilometers up Bukit Timah Road when three-year old Candy wanted to go to the toilet, so Dad stopped at a service station. The children all relieved themselves, and then took the opportunity to buy fizzy drinks from a slot machine. They piled back into the car, impatient to be off. Dad was still checking the engine, which was overheating. He filled the petrol tank, topped up the oil, and pumped up the tyres. After tinkering with the engine, he was rather oily and dirty.

Mother remembered with a shock that she had not cancelled

the newspapers, so she 'phoned their neighbour, Mrs Tai, to ask her to cancel them. After all, a heap of unread newspapers was the most obvious sign to burglars that a house was vacant. Poor Mrs Tai was awakened from her sleep at 5.30 a.m. by mother's inconsiderate call. By the time she got back in the car, the restless children were quarrelling again. Greg had shaken his fizzy drink which had then sprayed all over Sharleen's pretty new dress. Sharleen was in tears, and Dad was furious. Everyone was tired and tense and unhappy.

"OK," said Dad grimly. "We're going home." The children started crying and blaming each other. Mother looked very angry, but kept quiet. She knew better than to interrupt when Dad had that look on his face. "We're going back and starting this trip all over again. Nothing has gone right so far," explained Dad.

Back home, dawn was just breaking and a lovely sunrise welcomed them. They met the newspaper vendor just leaving their front gate and Mother cancelled the paper deliveries. Then she cooked a nourishing breakfast and they all ate sensibly, for they had worked up quite an appetite. Sharleen and Greg changed their clothes and Sharleen rinsed out the soiled dress and shirt without being asked. Greg delivered a flask of hot broth to Mrs Tai, along with a hastily written note from Mother, explaining that she had cancelled the paper and apologising for the early 'phone call. While the children were helping to clean up the breakfast dishes, Dad repacked the car more comfortably, giving the children more leg room. Then he made everyone (including himself) answer two questions: "What did I do that was not considerate? What can I do to make everything more enjoyable on this holiday?"

All co-operating as friends, they climbed back into the car, aware of how fragile tempers can be when people are tired, hungry and crowded. The family had sacrificed three hours of their holiday to make a new beginning, but they gained fourteen enjoyable days from the lesson they had learned.

A
1. Why did Dad and Mother want to make such an early start?
2. How did the family spend their evening before their departure?
3. What was disorganised about their departure?
4. Who was to blame for the confusion?

B
1. Describe the worst holiday or outing you have ever had. Could you have done anything to make it less unpleasant?
2. Describe the most enjoyable trip you have ever made. Who, or what, made it so enjoyable?
3. How can children and parents contribute towards a happy family trip?

C
1. Begin at the sentence, "Everybody was tired and tense and unhappy" (page 14, line 9), and write a different ending for the story from this point.
2. Imagine you are Mother. Write a letter to your sister in Kuala Lumpur, telling her about your family's holiday plans and asking if you might all stay with her. (Remember to begin and end your essay like a letter, and to give all the information that your sister would need to have.)

The House that Li Zhong Built

Li Zi Fa, a wealthy contractor, was returning to China to visit the village of his ancestors and meet his relatives. Starting off as a poor immigrant labourer, his grandfather had ended up with a small building supplies shop which he had passed on to his son. Zi Fa's father had expanded the business into a major construction company. Now the third generation was preparing the fourth generation to take over. Continuity in the family business and name were so important. Li had no son, but his daughter was soon to be married to his distant nephew, who was already managing one of Li's subsidiary companies.

Li Zi Fa prepared carefully for his journey to the motherland. He packed crates of sewing machines and bicycles, cans of food, bales of cloth and cases of clothing. He wanted to share some of his wealth and good fortune with his family in China.

Before leaving, he called his nephew, Li Zhong, to discuss the plans for a grand mansion to be built during his absence. "You have not headed such a large project before," said Zi Fa. "I am testing you, nephew. The man who commissioned this house is very rich and powerful. His instructions are that no expense be spared to make this the best residence in town."

"Leave it to me, Uncle," said Li Zhong confidently, and his uncle embraced him and departed on his journey.

Li Zhong, however, was the kind of young man who preferred a good time to hard work. He enjoyed parties and expensive hobbies and glamorous people. The new building was started. When the foundations were poured, Li Zhong was still lying in bed after a late night party. When the outer walls were erected, he was away on a yacht cruise. The subcontractors did a poor job as they lacked proper supervision.

17

Li Zhong's lifestyle was expensive and he had amassed enormous debts. Suddenly, he had a good idea to solve his financial problems. "I will substitute the quality materials that Uncle specified for substandard, cheap materials. Uncle's wealthy client will never notice the difference. Then I can use the difference to pay my gambling debts," he thought. So Li Zhong began cheating at every opportunity. The supporting columns had less cement and more sand than specified; the water pipes used for plumbing were of narrow gauge and inferior copper; the floorboards were not of treated timber; and the electrical wiring was not properly insulated. Li Zhong ignored the fact that the wiring was not even safe.

"No one, not even Uncle, will notice," chuckled Li Zhong to himself. "Once the walls are papered and painted, the house will look just like the plans and specifications. Feeling very clever, he pocketed the excess funds without the slightest feeling of guilt.

When his uncle returned from China, he and Li Zhong went to inspect the massive building. The old man ran his experienced eye over the puckered wallpaper and uneven flooring. He kicked the ugly piping under the handbasin and scratched some paint blobs on the ceramic wall tiles. He touched the rough varnish on the doors and tripped on a scuffed board near the front door.

Sadly, he said to Li Zhong, "I gave you this job to show that I accept and trust you with important work in our family business. Now I will tell you whom this mansion is for. I designed it myself and had it built as a wedding gift for my daughter and her prospective husband. I hope you are pleased with your present. As you build your house, so shall you live in it!"

A

1. Why did Li Zi Fa leave his nephew in charge of the building project?
2. Why did Li Zhong cheat his uncle? How did he cheat him? Whom was he really cheating?
3. How do we know that Li Zi Fa was not deceived by his nephew?

B

1. If you were Li Zi Fa's daughter and you had discovered what Li Zhong was doing, what would you have done?
2. "Honesty is the best policy." Discuss this statement. What does it mean? Is honesty always the best policy?
3. Can you think of other forms of cheating? (Remember, one can cheat morally, without stealing money or goods.)

C

1. Make up a similar short story in which the cheater finds that the one he has hurt most is himself.
2. You have just bought a new apartment. Write a letter to the contractor complaining about the poor workmanship and materials.

How Does Your Garden Grow?

Ahmad was a lonely old man. His wife had recently died and Ahmad had come to live with his son in a new village. Each morning his son left for work very early and came back late at night. Ahmad had nothing to do and no one to talk to. Every day he would walk up and down the street, hobbling along, bent low over his walking stick. He was bored and sad. He felt tired just walking to the end of the street. There he sat down outside the school, watching the boys kicking a football around the field. He enjoyed the sound of laughter and the youngsters yelling to each other, but the children ignored the old man. He would sit for hours outside the school gate, thinking back to his carefree childhood.

The principal, Mr Chen, noticed this regular visitor and felt sorry for the old man. He wondered how he could help him. Gardening was one of the school's extra curricular activities, and the headmaster observed the interested expression on Ahmad's face as he watched the students digging, raking and planting cuttings around the playground. Mr Chen had a flash of inspiration. There was a rocky strip of land outside the school fence. It looked untidy and was overgrown with *lallang*. One day, while supervising the gardening crew, the principal walked over to old Ahmad and greeted him.

"Do you like gardening?" he enquired.

"Oh yes," replied the wizened old fellow. "I love the feel of the soil." Ruefully he held up a gnarled old hand, crippled with arthritis. "These hands have nurtured many beautiful plants in their time," he said.

"We're trying to make our school look more attractive," said Mr Chen. "We would really appreciate your help in tending the front strip. It isn't really part of the school property, but it spoils the look of our school. You're welcome to use our tools and water. The hose will reach this far.''

Ahmad's wrinkled face lit up with anticipation and pleasure.

''You can plant whatever you like — anything that will thrive in this poor soil,'' added the principal.

So Ahmad began the task of transforming the strip of wilderness into a garden. He dug out the *lallang* and loosened the soil. He cleared out the stones and spread fertiliser, and then began collecting cuttings and seeds.

Now there was new purpose in the old man's life. His pace quickened and his posture improved. Instead of being more exhausted by the heavy physical work, he was invigorated by it. Ahmad began to speak to the villagers as he walked around, requesting cuttings from attractive bushes in the neighbourhood and seeds from pretty flowers. His little garden became his world and he pottered around contentedly every day. The school children were fascinated by his garden. Ahmad taught them to make little sunshades to protect delicate seedlings from the fierce sun. They exchanged cuttings and ideas. Passers-by began stopping to admire the now fertile strip. Soon the old man was surrounded by friends. Parents would pause and ask his advice about their own gardens. As his plants flourished, so did Ahmad. He was no longer a pathetic and depressed old widower. Now he was involved, busy, contented and needed. He had a useful job and enjoyed life once more.

During nature study classes, Ahmad was invited to demonstrate how to take a cutting and prepare soil for sowing. He showed the children how to prune fruit trees and transplant seedlings. He helped the boys collect insects for a science project. Ahmad became a familiar figure around the school. He cleaned and sharpened the gardening tools, mended broken equipment and became the school's general handymah. When the students were in class, he would linger in the canteen for a cool drink.

When Christmas came round, Ahmad was not forgotten. The students collected money to buy him a Christmas present. With tears in his eyes, the old man went on to the stage during an assembly to receive his gift of a new, shiny set of potting tools and packets of seeds.

Neither was Ahmad alone during the holidays, for he offered to care for all the school pets, as there was no one around the school. Primary Two had a cage of rabbits and Primary Four had an aquarium. Secondary One had cages of white mice and an injured bird. Other classes had turtles and frogs and there were two stray cats that lived near the canteen. Ahmad was happy to care for the pets, and even offered to keep the garden watered during the dry days. The school became his second home.

He was a generous old man. He gladly gave *pandan* leaves to ladies for their *nasi lemak*. The papayas from his strip of productive garden were shared among the children at recess. He gave chillies and limes to the teachers and when the *buah susu* vine covered the wire mesh with a gay profusion of purple flowers and tasty fruit, all his friends sampled them.

One day Ahmad walked proudly without his cane to the headmaster's office and knocked on the door. "This is my first water melon," he said to Mr Chen, handing over the heavy, succulent fruit. "I want you to have it. Thank you for lending me your garden."

A
1. Why did Ahmad feel bored and lonely?
2. What did Ahmad do every day when he first came to the village?
3. How did the children and the principal react to the old man?
4. Where was Ahmad's piece of land and what was it like at first?

5. Why was Ahmad able to transform it so easily and well into a fertile garden?
6. How did he make so many friends?
7. How did Ahmad look and feel before and after he had his garden?
8. Why do you think he gave the first water melon to Mr Chen?

B

1. Through his garden, Ahmad was able to become an active member of the community. How would you define 'an active member of a community'?
2. How can children and students become active members of their community?
3. What sort of people might feel lonely and depressed?
4. What is done and should be done to help lonely people?

C

1. Find out how many organisations help old people in Singapore and what help is given.
2. Write an essay entitled 'My Grandfather' or 'My Grandmother'.

Killer Litter

Killer litter has finally been highlighted and the authorities are cracking down on the culprits. But killer litter of a different nature has not been given such wide publicity. These are the cases involving cruelty to animals.

We are rightfully proud of our zoo; yet litter has literally killed many of the animals. There are countless examples of cruelty, both deliberate and unintentional:

*Kaiser, a favourite crocodile, died after not eating properly for nine months. Anxious zoo officials did all they could for him, including calling in the bomb disposal squad to x-ray him. Kaiser, it was discovered too late, had a metal drinking can blocking his stomach. Over nine miserable months, the poor creature starved to death, because of a thoughtless litter bug.

*Congo, a hippopotamus, sustained deep cuts on his tender foot pads from broken glass in his enclosure. Indeed, the trusting hippos appear fair game as they wallow in their pool and open their huge mouths to catch whatever object is thrown to them. They trust humans; yet visitors abuse their trust and think it amusing.

*A male ostrich was found battered to death.

*A gentle female Sana deer became ill and, despite all veterinary care, died. A post-mortem revealed that her intestines were choked with plastic bags — a horrible death and so unnecessary.

Have we become an uncaring public? The zoo has many signs requesting people *not* to feed the animals, and rubbish bins are placed strategically. Plastic cups have replaced canned and bottled drinks sold at the zoo, in an attempt to protect the animals. Now wax paper cups are being introduced, hopefully to save more animals from needless suffering and death.

25

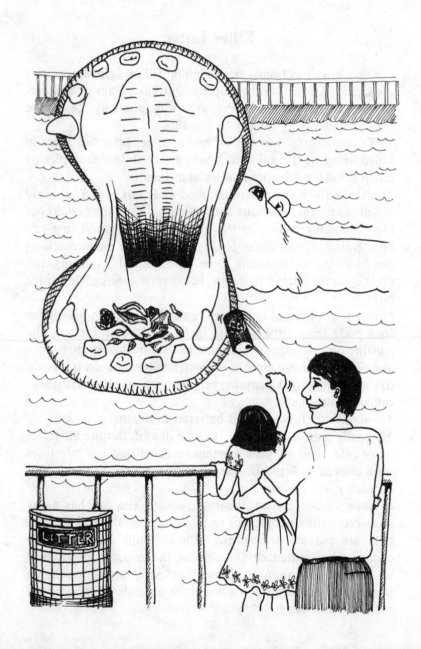

The Director of the zoo, Mr Bernard Harrison, feels that people want action. They come to see the animals perform. This is why the lethargic reptiles are usually such prime targets for abuse. "We hold regular shows and welcome visitors to see the animal antics," he said. "We have also introduced sessions where the public can meet tame animals and handle them."

But animal shows and direct contact with animals have not been sufficient to stamp out this desire for action which prompts such thoughtless and cruel behaviour. Zoos elsewhere have had similar experiences. A hippo was choked by a tennis ball. Bottlecaps galore have been found inside small animals. Razor blades were concealed inside bananas and fed to unsuspecting monkeys. This is sadistic, criminal behaviour!

So far, four offenders have been tried and fined for maltreating animals in Singapore. Perhaps we should consider making the penalties more severe to deter such antisocial behaviour. Generally, keepers and zoo staff hesitate to take legal action. They prefer to educate rather than prosecute, when the crime is due to ignorance rather than malice. However, if malicious intent or cruel behaviour is observed, zoo staff can evict members of the public, or detain them and call the police.

Generally, the young are learning to respect animals as living, feeling creatures. But you still see cruelty, as children experiment with animals at the zoo — right under the amused, indulgent gaze of their doting parents. Rabbits are yanked by their ears, young goats are thrown into their drinking trough, and wading birds are blinded by poking sticks. Parents chuckle in delight that their 'brave' little offspring dare to feed the big animals with plastic bags. These parents should be prosecuted for not preventing such cruelty to animals. Surely this is a sin of omission!

We have a fine zoo, a splendid collection of animals. We

have easy access to them and cheap entry fees. The zoo brings nature within reach of all Singaporeans. As city-dwellers, we should treasure this link with the natural world. We must not stand by complacently and lose it.

If killer litter continues to take its toll on our helpless animals, we will require more keepers to patrol the zoo and there will be fewer chances for animal-human interaction. Greater barriers will be erected to protect the animals from us, not us from them. (Man seems to be the only animal that wounds and kills for fun.) All this extra security would mean higher fees and less chance to enjoy our zoo and animals.

So, while we campaign against killer litter among our high-rise flats, let's extend the same protection and security to our animals.

A

1. Give at least two examples of death caused at the zoo by littering.
2. Give two examples of deliberate cruelty to animals mentioned in this article.
3. What kind of parents does the author criticise?
4. What will happen to the zoo if the animals continue to die from killer litter and cruelty?

B

1. Have you ever seen an animal being mistreated? What did you do about it?
2. Have you ever adopted a stray animal?
3. What would you do if you saw people feeding the zoo animals or teasing them?

C

1. Imagine you have witnessed a case of cruelty to a stray dog. Write a police report stating details of the incident and suggesting ways of dealing with this problem.

2. Write a letter to the editor of *The Straits Times,* recommending ways the zoo can protect animals in captivity from cruel visitors. Include suggestions for punishing offenders.
3. Imagine you are one of the injured animals. Describe how it feels to be bullied and tortured.

Down the Slippery Road

"It's so easy — go on! We got away with it the last time," urged David.

"No, it's stealing," argued Jim.

"Oh come on, don't be a spoil sport! The shopkeeper's so rich and we're hungry. Anyway, think how much profit he's made out of our class this term," said David.

"It's only a bar of chocolate. He won't even miss it," encouraged Sam.

Jim felt nervous paying only for the peanuts. The chocolate felt heavy and hard in his pocket, and he was sure other people could see it. But the boys didn't get caught.

"See, it's easy," the gang boasted. "You're just a coward, afraid of being found out." They taunted him and bragged about their thefts until Jim felt quite left out.

"It's wrong," he repeated stubbornly. "I feel so guilty that I'll never dare go back to that shop."

Slowly, the boys pressured him to join them in another of their adventures. "Come on, Jim, it's just for kicks. We dare you to do it." Finally, Jim submitted, against his better judgement. This time the boys picked a department store. A silver lighter, a Swiss army knife and a compass were their targets. Jim was to acquire the pocket knife while the others distracted the sales assistants. It was easier this time. His palms were not so damp and his heart wasn't pounding so furiously. He sauntered out of the store with his friends, feeling quite clever and enjoying their admiration of his bravado.

His conscience was becoming dulled. Soon he was lifting books from the local library, then dumping them in a rubbish chute, because the boys had lost their library cards. Jim was finding the dishonest way easy to fall into.

"Where did you get this pocket knife?" asked his Dad one day.

"Er...I won it in a game of marbles," mumbled Jim.

"Where did this army T-shirt come from?" enquired Mum, puzzled as she was doing the laundry one morning.

"I exchanged it with David for my brown shirt, the one that's too tight," lied Jim. (Actually, he had lost the brown shirt at the swimming pool and had stolen the army T-shirt from the changing room.)

Little lies led to bigger lies. Soon Jim was caught in such a web of untruths that he couldn't remember what he said to whom, and life became very complicated. Then one day Jim was chosen to do the most dangerous dare of all — to steal money from the science teacher's drawer. He was rather scared, but the others persuaded him, saying that this was the only way they could see the new Rambo movie. Jim wanted the approval of his friends so much that he finally gave in and agreed to steal the money.

He lingered after class, hoping to see where Mr Wu, the science teacher, kept the key to his desk drawer. He left it on a hook just inside the staffroom. Jim had to carry books there for another teacher every recess; so it was easy just to lift the key the next day.

After their next science lesson, Jim was feeling quite bold. He loitered around sharpening pencils until the classroom was empty. With a furtive look round, Jim swiftly moved to the teacher's desk. In moments he had $27 in single notes and coins stuffed in his pencil case. He dumped it in his schoolbag and ran out into the bright sunlight.

What a panic next day when the theft was discovered! The headmaster called a special assembly and appealed to the boys to co-operate in exposing the thief. "Loyalty to friends is no excuse," he said. "That money had been collected to help a poor student pay for his science books." The guilty boys wriggled uncomfortably. Jim felt terrible and lowered his head, trying to hide his burning face. How he regretted what he had done. He wandered miserably back to class.

During recess, Jim was approached by Abang, the school caretaker. "Jim, I noticed you alone in the science classroom yesterday. You were the last to leave," said old Abang gravely. "The headmaster is going to call the police if the culprit doesn't own up. When the police question me, I will have to tell them that I saw you." The kindly man leaned heavily on his broom and watched Jim's shifty gaze. "Why did you do it, boy?"

"My friends would have called me a sissy. They would have said I was a chicken unless I carried out the dare," mumbled Jim.

"Do you think it's clever to deprive a poor student of his science books? He helps his parents every night after school and all weekend at their hawker stall. Still this boy makes time to study. Do you really want to take money from someone like him?"

Hot tears stung Jim's eyes. He blinked and shook his head.

"Let's go and confess to the headmaster," said Abang kindly. "I'll come with you. You'll be punished — you deserve that — but it's better to get off the slippery road to dishonesty now. It's not too late to make amends and start again."

A
1. Why did Jim agree to steal the chocolate?
2. How did he feel on the first and second occasions he stole from a shop?
3. What did he lie to his parents about?
4. Why was it so easy for Jim to steal the money?
5. How did he feel at assembly, and why?

6. Who suspected that Jim was the thief?
7. What did he do about his suspicions?

B

1. Whose fault was it that Jim became a thief?
2. Are our actions and behaviour influenced by the opinions of our friends?
3. Have your friends ever made you do something you did not want to do?
4. Did Abang do the right thing?
5. Should Jim take all the blame, or should he tell the headmaster about his friends' involvement?
6. Is there such a thing as a 'white lie'?
7. What do you think his parents' reaction was when they found out?
8. What do you think would be the most suitable punishment for Jim?

C

1. Compose an imaginary conversation between Jim and his parents when they find out. (First, decide what sort of parents Jim has: kind and understanding, or hard and strict.)
2. Write an essay entitled 'The Pickpocket'.

The Sounds of Progress

Granny sighed as she reminisced. "Ten years ago, I would sit in my old rattan chair listening to the birds. How clearly I remember the comforting sounds of *kampung* life in Jalan Timun. There was the swish-swish of the *sapu* lady sweeping the streets and the scratching of her woven basket. The little old woman always had a cheery word for me as she did her daily rounds. In the distance, I could sometimes hear the faint calls of the *karang-guni* man (the junk collector) and the village children as they raced off to trade with him. Occasionally the *taik lembu* truck would call...the smell was rather strong. We regularly bought their fertilizer, because we grew delicious papayas, mangoes, rambutans and nankas; really mouth-watering.

"We were woken at dawn by the crowing of the roosters, who thought nothing of strutting into the house in search of food. One little hen was especially tame, and laid her eggs in an old box alongside my chair. Sometimes the mosque beat the roosters with their daybreak call of the faithful to prayer.

"Dogs barked, babies cooed or whimpered, older children laughed and shouted. Ducks and geese added to the happy, friendly sounds of this little world.

"We looked forward to the tinkling bell of the ice-cream vendor. On hot days, the children would fetch me a cone for 5¢. Itinerant hawkers all announced their arrival in different ways. When durian was in season, the seller could be smelt long before he appeared. The mee sellers, with their distinctive clacketty-clack rhythm, came often and the delicious smell of their noodles would waft towards the wooden porch, where I passed the days fanning myself, and listening to the village gossip.

"In the rainy season, we would all seek refuge indoors and

board up the entrance to our houses, for flooding was bad. Our house was often flooded and I would have to wade through the living room very cautiously to go to the bathroom. The children would have a great time out in the flooded streets, helping to push cars which had stalled — for a fee, of course. They would splash around in the muddy water, while the women mopped up and hung things out to dry.

"Some evenings we could hear the loudspeakers from a *wayang* or some neighbourhood celebration. Births and weddings were joyful events; the whole village helped with the preparations. Of course, no one minded the extra noise late at night, for all were invited...Funerals too. All the adults would keep awake to comfort the bereaved family. There was a sense of belonging in those days.

"On their way back from the market, the women would pass with their babies slung on their hips, complaining about the increase in prices. I felt useful and needed as the youngsters gathered around my chair, begging '*Ninek*' to tell them stories of long ago...

"Now my kampung has been bulldozed. Skyscrapers and motorways have replaced the huts and muddy lanes.

"I still sit in my rocking chair, but now the breeze is through the grille of my flat on the fifteenth floor. The sounds and smells are different now. Sometimes the pungent smells of frying *blachan* or salted fish waft up from the flat below. Most evenings the sweet aroma of incense permeates the air.

"I hear lorries revving their engines, and rubbish trucks grinding and digesting their loads. Jumbo jets roar overhead and the resounding clang of dusty pile-drivers rends the air. Upstairs I hear someone practising the piano, and he never improves. Every morning I am awakened by my alarm clock. Then I hear a systematic pounding immediately above, and I imagine the delicious *sambal tumis* that is being prepared.

"Every night there are TV and HiFi sets competing with

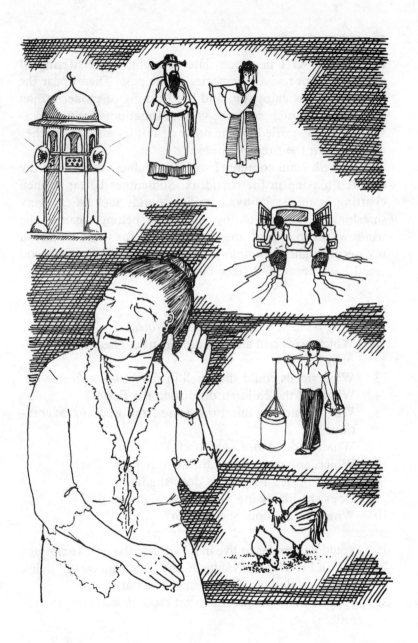

each other. As I lie alone, late at night, the clattering of mahjong chips revives memories of the past. Then I hear the gurgle of baths emptying, and the flushing of modern toilet cisterns. No more hole-in-the-ground squat-pots for us. Occasionally I am startled by the noise of bottles and tins as they clatter down the rubbish chute.

"Ah well, I am content. I still hear babies crying, and the children playing in the corridors. Sometimes I hear women chatting or men arguing. Familiar sounds such as crockery smashing, thunder roaring and rain pelting against the windows mean a lot to me. I thank God for these sounds in my sterile, highrise *kampung*. Silence would terrify me — you see, I have been blind since birth."

A

1. Why is noise so important to '*Ninek*'?
2. Which birds and animals did she use to hear in the *kampung*?
3. What smells could she smell in the *kampung*?
4. What did the children do during the floods?
5. Why did no one mind the noise from wedding celebrations?
6. What made '*Ninek*' feel useful?
7. Which noises does she dislike in her new flat?
8. Which noises and smells does she like?
9. Does she like living in her new high-rise flat?
10. Which senses does she rely on?

B

1. Would you prefer to live in a high-rise flat or a *kampung*?
2. Make a list of the advantages and disadvantages of living (a) in a *kampung*, (b) in a high-rise flat.
3. What do blind people use to get around, and how do they read?

4. What special problems do blind people have?
5. How can you help blind people?

C

1. Put on a blindfold and try to:
    (a) do familiar things, e.g. comb your hair, tie your shoelaces, or sharpen a pencil.
    (b) find your way from the classroom door to your desk.
    (c) unpack your bag, identify the different books and objects, and count your money.
    (d) identify three of your friends by touch.
2. Imagine you are blind and write an essay entitled 'A Day in my Life'.

When Strangers Came to Town

The referee blew his whistle. Singapore had won the cup, 2 — 0, over Negeri Sembilan! The Seremban stadium errupted as supporters and players alike went wild with delight. This called for a *real* celebration, not the tea party provided by the hosts; that was too tame and stifling. "On our way through Johor let's go for a sea-food binge," someone suggested; so the rowdy young men clambered aboard their bus yelling, singing and telling rude jokes. A few of the guys settled at the back of the bus and began passing bottles of liquor amongst themselves. They knew Coach would be furious but, emboldened by the bravado which comes from being one of the gang, they took turns, swigging deeply from the bottles.

By the time the bus reached Johor, they were high-spirited and reckless. Fortunately, at that hour of night, the restaurant was almost empty, so the group's rowdy behaviour didn't upset too many diners. They feasted on prawns, squid, crabs and fish. They laughed and joked around, spilling food over the formica tables, and swinging precariously on their metal stools.

Coach ordered durian for desert and the long-suffering owner, Mr Ali, trundled out a barrowload full of the pungent fruit. Then, the boys who had been drinking began tossing a heavy durian like a ball. With loud guffaws, more joined in and the durian was tossed more wildly. Raju tripped as he lunged for the thorny fruit and the spiky durian hit his face hard, blinding him. He yelped in pain as he stumbled backwards, crashing into a window. He lay unconscious, bleeding heavily as his friends gathered anxiously around. Mr Ali took one look at the gaping gashes and 'phoned his friend, Dr Qiu, who lived nearby.

"Don't move him," instructed Dr Qiu. "I'm on my way

over right now." Although it was after midnight, Dr Qiu had not gone to bed. He had been making last minute preparations for his son's wedding the next day. The whole family was converging on Johor for the big event, and the bride's family had travelled all the way from Canada for the wedding.

"I won't be long, dear," called Dr Qiu to his wife. "You get some sleep. There's been a bad accident down at Ali's place." He grabbed his medical bag and climbed into his battered old car and drove off.

Raju had regained consciousness by the time the doctor arrived. He had several nasty puncture wounds around his left eye, where the durian had hit him. It was very swollen and an ugly purple colour. Raju was in pain, with a lump on his head and several deep cuts from the broken glass. Gently Dr Qiu bathed the wounds and bandaged them up. He gave Raju a painkiller so the bumpy journey home by bus would not distress him.

The footballers were not joking any more; in fact, they all felt rather foolish. Their coach offered to pay Dr Qiu, but he waved away the money and said he hoped the boys had learned their lesson. Coach paid Ali for the meal and the broken window, while Dr Qiu tiredly packed his bag and headed for home and a well-earned rest.

The road was under repair and poorly lit. Even at 2 a.m. heavy goods trucks thundered along, making long-haul deliveries between Singapore and Kuala Lumpur. As the doctor carefully negotiated a sharp bend, he never knew what hit him...

A heavily laden timber lorry took the turning too fast, swerving right into the doctor's path. There was a screech of brakes, a dreadful thud, the smashing of glass and tearing of metal, then an eerie silence that seemed to last for ever.

A bus was travelling along the same road, not far behind.

It stopped when the driver saw the enormous truck straddling the road. Logs had burst their safety chains on impact and had rolled off the truck, pinning the driver into his wrecked car. More logs covered the road. In the glare of the bus lights you could see the horribly twisted remains of a battered Ford.

"Let's see what we can do to help, boys," yelled the coach. The football team climbed out of their bus, eager to help. They tugged at the logs and tried to extricate the driver from the mangled wreck. "Oh God!" came a horrified whisper from Raju. "It's the nice doctor!"

It was the worst accident they had ever seen. Some of the men wept at the sight of the crushed body which had been a fine, helpful doctor just moments earlier.

The doctor's partner — his son — was called to the scene. He had the nightmare of discovering that the crash victim was his own beloved father. Then, in the early hours of what should have been the happiest day of his life, young Dr Qiu had the heart-breaking job of telling his mother that her husband was dead, killed on their son's wedding day. What should have been a happy family celebration became a numbing, sorrowful funeral.

The football team sent flowers and Raju and the coach attended the funeral. Raju was still heavily bandaged, but would not lose his sight, thanks to Dr Qiu's prompt and skilful attention. Raju felt like a murderer. The Johor people were deeply distressed. For thirty years old Dr Qiu had loved and served the villagers, and in another generation they would probably still talk of the tragedy. They won't forget the night that a bunch of rowdy strangers came to town to celebrate a football victory — and indirectly caused the death of an innocent man.

A

1. What did the Singapore team decide to do to celebrate their victory?

2. Why were they noisy, high-spirited and reckless?
3. What did some of them do with a durian?
4. Describe Raju's accident.
5. How do we know that Dr Qiu was a kind and conscientious man?
6. Describe Dr Qiu's accident.
7. Why was his death doubly tragic?

B

1. What effect does alcohol have on the body? What other substances and activities can be harmful?
2. What is gang bravado? Is it a good or a bad thing? Why?
3. When did the victory celebration get out of hand? Who could have controlled the merriment? What could he have done or said? How would you try to quieten a rowdy, reckless group of friends?
4. What should you do if you witness an accident in which people are injured?
5. How did Raju feel about Dr Qiu's death? How could he repay his debt to the doctor?

C

1. Imagine you are a newspaper reporter. Write an account of the road accident, giving background information on Dr Qiu.
2. Imagine you were one of the men in the Singapore team. Write a letter of condolence to Mrs Qiu and her family. (Make up suitable addresses for yourself and Mrs Qiu.)

Father's Day

Today was Father's day again. Dad had picked Steve up at 8 a.m. and they had gone to the hawker centre for breakfast. Later, they had gone fishing and caught two tiny fish at Ponggol, had a swim and built a sandcastle. Then Father had taken Steve shopping. "Your shoes are a disgrace, son, and that shirt's too tight. Let's get some new ones," suggested Dad. Money was no object to him. The shirt that mother had carefully mended and repaired so many times was left at the shop and Steve walked out in smart new clothes. They browsed in the book store for a while, and Dad bought all the comics and the new war book Steve wanted. Steve was fascinated by soldiers and battles, warships and fighter planes, and spent hours constructing model tanks and jeeps for imaginary wars. Somehow it was reassuring to know that other people had fights, not just his parents.

At 5 p.m. Dad took Steve home, laden with gifts. Dad was like Father Christmas. Steve knew he could get anything he wanted by cajoling Dad, especially since his parents had separated.

Mother coldly surveyed the gifts as Steve crept into the house. She snatched the comics and tossed them down the rubbish chute. "No son of mine is going to read such trash," she said firmly. "It's just like your father to fill your mind with nonsense."

"What did you have for lunch?" she enquired later as they ate a simple homecooked meal. "A hotdog? I guessed as much. Junk-food, no nutritious value. He doesn't know what's good for you. Now tell me about your day. I spent all morning cleaning." She started clearing up the dinner dishes. Steve muttered a few brief details about their day's adventures, while his mother bustled around the kitchen washing the dishes. She always seemed too busy and pre-occupied to stop and listen — really listen to him. "She only hears what she wants to hear," thought Steve sadly.

"What, so many hours in the sun? It's too tiring for you," grumbled Mother, catching only the thread of his account. "Now I'll have to boil barley water for you to drink. Really, that man is so irresponsible."

Steve retreated to his room. It was neat and tidy, just as Mother expected it to be. She seemed obsessed with cleanliness these days. Sometimes it seemed as if she was trying to wash away all her memories of the past, mused Steve to himself. He felt old and very sad. Mum was lonely and he was lonely. Why couldn't they communicate? She was so withdrawn and critical these days. She avoided their old friends; and there was an invisible barrier between them. But why? Steve pondered this question many times and never found an answer. He longed for her to reach out and be affectionate, he so much wanted her understanding.

Steve began to dread Father's day, because there was always an interrogation about Mother. Dad wanted a blow-by-blow account of whom she saw and what she did and where she went. Steve felt helpless and frustrated; he was always stuck in the middle. He felt like the ball in a game of soccer; being kicked from one goalpost to the other. Both parents claimed they loved him; but Steve felt thoroughly unloved.

Slowly, Steve developed a bad habit. At first he did not exactly tell lies, he just avoided the truth. When Dad asked if Mum went out at night, Steve pleaded ignorance. "I don't know," was easier than answering all sorts of questions about her whereabouts. Steve resented being used as a spy. He felt torn between two loyalties, so in the only way he knew how, Steve protected everyone, including himself, by stretching the truth. White lies and half truths became easier and easier. He planned his answers and evaded questions. Some-

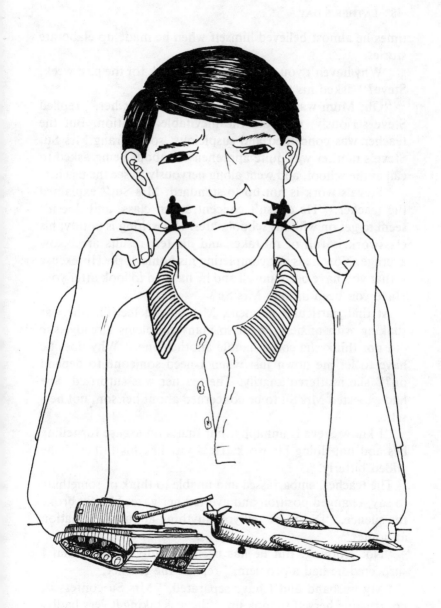

times he almost believed himself when he made up elaborate stories.

"Why haven't you done your homework for the past week, Steve?" asked his teacher one day.

"Oh, Mum was ill, and I had to look after her," replied Steve seriously, to avoid the inevitable detention. But the teacher was concerned and suspicious, so she rang Mrs Su. Steve's mother was quite apprehensive about being asked to call at the school, and went along nervously to see the teacher.

"Steve's work is not up to standard, Mrs Su," explained the teacher. "He doesn't concentrate in class, and doesn't seem to get on with his schoolmates. His writing is untidy; his classwork is full of mistakes and his test results are below average. Now he is not completing his homework. His excuse is that you have been unwell and he has had to look after you. Have you been unwell, Mrs Su?

At that particular moment, Mrs Su did feel ill. She was shaking with anxiety. With so many problems already, she did not think she could handle another one. "Why does he have to let me down just when I need someone to depend on?" she muttered angrily. The teacher was surprised. She had expected Mrs Su to be concerned about her son, not herself.

"I know Steve is unhappy, but that's no excuse for telling lies and not doing his work. He's just like his father!" she added bitterly.

The teacher, embarrassed and unable to think of something to say, changed position and averted her gaze. Mrs Su broke the silence. "Did Steve tell you anything about the situation at home?"

"No. Nothing. But he has been so badly behaved that I suspected he had a problem," replied the teacher.

"My husband and I have separated," Mrs Su confessed, not trusting herself to look up. "Steve is taking it very badly.

I have custody of my son and he spends Sundays with his father.''

"I think, Mrs Su, that Steve wants to be loyal to both you and your husband, but feels guilty when by doing so he upsets one or other of you. Feelings like these are very common among children from broken homes,'' explained the teacher. "It's only natural for a child to love both parents.''

"I suppose I'm angry with his father and expect him to be loyal only to me,'' admitted Mrs Su. "Could you speak to Steve's father and make him see how we're both hurting Steve by making him feel guilty. He doesn't listen to me.''

"Yes, I'll speak to Steve's father, and I'll try to help Steve too. But you must try not to criticise your husband in front of him. And listen to Steve's opinions,'' said the teacher kindly.

"Steve's a sensible boy, and I really depend on him,'' said Mrs Su. "But I suppose I've been so pre-occupied with my own problems that I've neglected him. He must be feeling hurt and rejected too.''

"Yes, Steve is a good boy at heart,'' agreed the teacher. "You've both been through a rough time, but the worst is over now. Let Steve enjoy Sundays with his father; he needs both his parents. You can make Sunday a special Mother's day too, and have a well earned rest while Steve's away.''

A
1. Describe Steve's day with his father.
2. Describe his life at home with his mother.
3. Why did Steve start telling lies?
4. Why was his teacher concerned about him?

B
1. How do you think Steve felt when his parents argued?
2. Do you think it is better for parents to separate if they can't live together peacefully?

3. Should parents inform the school if there is a family crisis?
4. Why was Steve untruthful?
5. What is resentment?
6. Are 'white lies' or half truths ever justified?

C

1. Imagine you are Steve. Write a letter to your father explaining how you feel.
2. What do you think Mrs Su said to Steve after she had spoken to his teacher. Write an imaginary dialogue.

The Cat Burglar

It was before dawn when Jeffrey heard the noise. He was stumbling to the bathroom half asleep. "I must be dreaming," he thought, yawning and rubbing his eyes. Then he heard the strange sounds again. Taking a torch in one hand and a heavy brass ornament in the other, Jeffrey crept downstairs. He was wide awake now and his heart was pounding. What intruder was making those whining noises and scratching sounds? Was it a burglar?

Jeffrey paused in the stillness. Noises again. He raised the ornament and flicked on the torch. There in the light was a startled tabby cat, her eyes wide with fright. Instead of running away, she arched her back and hissed threateningly.

Relieved that it was only a cat, Jeffrey moved closer and saw three tiny newborn kittens tangled together, still damp and bloodstreaked from birth. "Perhaps there will be more kittens," thought Jeffrey. He went into the kitchen and poured some milk into a saucer, then placed it near the storeroom under the stairs. "Here, cat, drink this," he said softly, and went upstairs to get some more sleep.

Several hours later, Jeffrey went downstairs again, to make a cup of coffee and collect the newspaper. He found one cold little kitten miaowing piteously. "What a loud noise for such a tiny bundle of fur to make," thought Jeffrey. He felt guilty about frightening the mother away during the night and responsible for the welfare of the kitten. He wondered what had happened to the others. Warming some milk in a dish, he rummaged through the first-aid kit until he found an eye dropper. He washed it carefully and picked up the blind kitten. Its legs flailed desperately, with little claws grabbing at anything they could hold. Jeffrey took an old towel and wrapped it securely around the kitten, holding it gently face

51

upward. He dribbled the eye dropper of milk over the little mouth. The kitten glugged and gurgled, struggling to get free. Jeffrey tried over and over again to feed it, but more milk went over the little face and soaked into the towel, than into the kitten.

Jeffrey was late for work. He noticed that the milk saucer was empty, so he filled it again and hoped that the mother cat would return to her baby. He lined a box with rags and snuggled the kitten inside. Leaving the front window ajar, he went off to the office.

While Jeffrey had been asleep, mother cat had been hard at work. After licking her newborn kittens clean, she had gulped down the saucer of milk and gone to find a new home for her family. She did not feel safe with that man and his bright light.

Two doors away, the solid front door of an identical terrace house was open. Only the collapsible gate was shut and she slipped easily between the bars. Mother cat made a quick survey inside the house. All was quiet. She found a cupboard full of shoes. It was dark and safe inside. She scampered back to Jeffrey's house and fed her babies. Then she took the largest, grasping it firmly in her mouth, and leapt up to Jeffrey's window-sill. She squeezed through the iron grille and jumped down to the ground without dropping her precious burden. She padded along the deserted street to No. 9, through the iron gate and into the shoe cupboard in the storeroom. Depositing her kitten there, she hurried back to collect kitten number two, carrying it the same way by the scruff of its neck. When the two were safely nestled together, she went back for her weakling. She peeped cautiously through the window and saw Jeffrey handling her baby. Mother cat watched fearfully. Eventually the man put her kitten into a box and as soon as he departed, mother cat was alongside her kitten, licking her comfortingly and cleaning the milk off her face and fur.

She noticed that the saucer was again full of milk and she lapped it up eagerly. Now she took the last kitten firmly by the neck and leapt out of the window. She trotted down the road to No. 9. Exhausted, she lay in the shoe cupboard, stretched out on old sneakers, while her three hungry babies clawed at her soft belly. Their tiny pink mouths nuzzled clumsily, rooting for her nipples and warm milk. Totally blind, they were very dependent on her.

Jeffrey stopped at the provision shop on his way home from work and bought a tin of powdered milk for his new pet. When he found that the baby had disappeared, he was both disappointed and at the same time relieved that the mother had not abandoned her kitten.

As he slumped in front of the television that evening, with his feet on the coffee table, he was aware of being observed. There on the window ledge, peeping between the pot plants, was the tabby cat with her funny striped face. Jeffrey talked quietly to the cat. He moved slowly to the kitchen so that she would not be startled and filled the saucer with milk. He placed it on a newspaper beside the box where he had put the kitten, and went upstairs to bed. In the morning, he refilled the saucer before work, knowing that if the mother was well fed, she would nourish her babies. He was pleased to find the saucer empty by the evening. Thus, Jeffrey's friendship with the stray cat began.

Meanwhile, the occupants of No. 9 had returned home. While mother cat was outside devouring a mouse, their car pulled up. Children were squabbling; a baby was crying; adults with loud voices were disturbing the peaceful refuge. Before long a lady discovered the kittens in their shoe cupboard.

"Come here, children, see what I've found," called the lady excitedly.

Soon the kittens were being cuddled and carried by the children. The lady prepared a big box lined with lots of old rags. "This will be a much better home for our kittens than that smelly shoe cupboard," she declared.

The kind-hearted lady opened a tin of tuna fish and put half the fish on a plate for the mother cat. She was hiding in the yard, anxiously waiting for an opportunity to rescue her babies from this human invasion. Finally, the family went upstairs and mother cat dashed back to her kittens. She let them suckle until they fell asleep, then she gobbled down the tuna fish, and went prowling around the neighbourhood, hunting for a new home.

Next day, at No. 13, the residents were sitting down to eat dinner when they heard some thuds and bumps in the loft. "It must be rats again," grumbled Dad. "I'll call the rodent control men."

When the pest exterminators arrived the following day, they used a long ladder and climbed up into the roof with torches and tins of rat bait. A few minutes later one of the men poked his dusty face through the trap door in the ceiling and said, "Mrs Wang, your husband complained that the rats made so much noise that they must be the size of cats. Well, I've news for you — they *are* cats! A whole family has taken up residence. Do you want us to remove them?"

"How did they get in?" asked Mrs Wang, laughing. "I suppose if the mother could get in, she can find her way out again. No, don't move them. They'll keep the mice away."

Mother cat was very contented. Her babies were snug and safe and warm. They had the whole loft to themselves. Every day Mrs Wang put meat and rice in a bowl in the back garden and she would call to mother cat to come and eat it.

The cat did not forget her other supporters. Every morning and evening she visited Jeffrey at No. 5 and lapped up her saucer of milk. Then she would go to No. 9 for a feast of tuna

fish before hurrying back to No. 13 to feed her growing family. She was more bold these days and let the humans speak to her, but she would never get near enough for them to touch her, for she was a wild cat.

The kittens thrived and grew rapidly. Their eyes opened and their fur grew. They scampered about in the loft, chasing each other. When their mother was away too long, they would miaow and cry loudly. Soon they needed meat and exercise; milk was no longer sufficient. Mother cat taught them how to catch mice. She took them out on to the hot metal awning and showed them how to stalk birds. She let them play with cockroaches and catch flies. After six weeks of caring for her little ones, she knew it was time for them to go out into the world and fend for themselves.

She gave her kittens a final feed and licked them tenderly. Then she took the biggest kitten in her mouth, hopped down on to a brick fence and scrambled over a pile of boxes. She stopped to get a better grasp on her load, then carried kitty back to the milk dish beside the place where he was born. "This is your home now," she seemed to miaow to kitten number one. Mother cat took the second kitten by the same route and she deposited her most playful baby at house No. 9. Her plump and mischievous baby would enjoy all the love and attention of the noisy family. He would have fun with the children.

The smallest kitten, who was rather weak still, was brought down and placed inside a big leather shoe by the back door of No. 13. It was here that Mrs Wang found the kitten when she opened the door. How delighted she was to have a little kitten to fuss over and spoil. Mother cat watched as Mrs Wang dipped her finger in milk, letting the kitten lick it from her finger as she guided her nose to the saucer.

For several days mother cat visited all three houses to check on her kittens. She spied on them through windows and doors as their respective families fed and played with their new pets. Eventually she was satisfied that she had placed her babies in caring homes, so she went back to her life of scavenging in rubbish bins.

(This is a true story based on the author's and her neighbours' experiences.)

A
1. Who owned the mother cat?
2. Why did she leave No. 5?
3. What was wrong with No. 9?
4. Why was No. 13 a better home?
5. Was mother cat a good mother? Give reasons to support your opinion.
6. What did she do with her kittens when they grew old enough to be left on their own?

B
1. Which other animals care for their young very well?
2. What would you do if you found a litter of kittens in your home?
3. Should we feed and care for stray animals?
4. Is it kinder sometimes to take them to the SPCA?
5. What does 'SPCA' stand for? Who runs it and how is it financed?
6. What does the SPCA do with stray animals? Is it cruel to put them to sleep?

C
1. Imagine you are one of the kittens. Describe how you adjusted to living with a family and becoming domesticated.
2. Imagine you are Jeffrey, *or* the kind-hearted lady at No. 9, *or* Mrs Wang at No. 13. Prepare a few notes and then tell the class about your experiences with mother cat and her kittens.

The Christmas Tree

Nirmala was ten years old, but she was so small and frail that people thought she was only five. She was born with a damaged heart; she was a 'blue baby'. Her father had been killed by communist terrorists when she was very young.

Nirmala enjoyed watching other children playing and wished she could join them, chasing butterflies and romping with the dog. She was a very good listener, so she heard many exciting stories of adventures around the tea plantation where she lived. Sometimes the tea-pluckers would bring back a huge python from the hills, or trap a snake that was stealing their chickens. Occasionally her friends would catch an ugly rhinoceros beetle or a beautiful butterfly for her. Her collection included soft feathers, a dead scorpion and a snake casting. She kept all these special treasures in a teabox under her camp bed.

During the day when everyone except Jamal, the old blind man, had gone out to the fields, Nirmala would take out her treasure chest and gently hold up the delicate butterflies to watch the sun's rays through their transparent wings. She would describe to Jamal the beauty and colour in her butterflies and insects. Jamal said that she was like a dainty butterfly, for she was so delicate and tired so easily.

Sometimes a few chickens would visit her hut, pecking and clucking as they scratched the dirt floor, hunting for food. Occasionally a *kampung* dog would come in and Nirmala enjoyed talking to him and cuddling him. She even used her mother's tortoise-shell comb to comb his wiry, shaggy coat. She called this funny, lop-eared mongrel 'Parum' and pretended that he was her very own pet. Nirmala hid small bits of vegetables and rice from her dinner and saved bones from the meat her mother sometimes cooked. Parum always seemed to be hungry and the more she fed him, the more regularly he visited her.

Every morning, before dawn, her mother and aunt rose, tidied their simple shack, bathed Nirmala and prepared food for the day. They would cover Nirmala's portion and leave it on the table, and take their share to the fields in a *tingkat*. As the sun rose in the sky, they would trudge up the long track to the tea plantation's drying and crushing plant to collect huge woven rattan baskets. Their *kepala* would instruct them which hillside they were to work on. All day they would bend, plucking the tender young leaves and shoots from the tea-plants. On a good day, when there was no rain, Nirmala's mother could fill two baskets, which, when tightly packed, weighed 35 kilos each — more than Nirmala herself weighed!

Nirmala was very lonely during the daytime. She looked forward to her mother and aunty returning in the evenings. She longed to talk and wanted to hear all the village gossip, but usually the adults were so tired that they just wanted to bathe, eat and sleep.

Each day Nirmala found it harder to walk to the *kampung* tap to wash the clothes. She stopped and rested very often on the way, but she was still quite breathless. Sometimes it took almost a day to wash their few tatty clothes and she would have no time to study her hoard of treasures. Sometimes Parum would go with her. She enjoyed his company. He would run on ahead, sniffing and wagging his stumpy brown tail, barking at the chickens who would flap and squawk loudly, scattering in fear. But Parum never hurt the chickens, and as Nirmala dragged her way slowly along the track, she would collect the feathers they left behind.

Some of the villagers grew flowers: beautiful pink geraniums, yellow and mauve chrysanthemums, and other sweet smelling blossoms. Every day several truckloads of flowers were carefully wrapped in tissue paper and boxed for the long journey to Kuala Lumpur and even Singapore. The truckers talked of life in the big cities, where buses and trains rushed by, carrying crowds of people. Nirmala had never seen a train and couldn't imagine anything bigger than the flower trucks. She had never been out of her *kampung* on the vast tea plantation and she couldn't imagine what real heat was like. The highlands where she lived were cool and damp and misty. Sometimes, when it was very foggy and she was struggling to breathe, Nirmala would hear the village elders whispering that if only they could earn enough money to send her to the hot dry coast, she would feel less ill and miserable.

Some of the plantation children had been down to Tanah Ratah, the biggest village in the Cameron Highlands, for their fathers had saved enough money to buy a motor scooter. As many as four members of a family would perch precariously on one of these noisy wonder-machines and bump and rattle their way down the mountain tracks and winding roads. They would return full of interesting stories of life in the town, where rich people put ten cent coins into a magic machine called a juke box that played music, while they drank coffee and ate *roti prata* at the *kedai*. It sounded so exciting that Nirmala's eyes lit up with interest as she listened, fascinated by their stories.

At Christmas time, Nirmala's best friend, Madiah, went down to the town in a truck carrying fresh vegetables. She took along a collection of beetles and butterflies she had patiently collected all year long. The tourists would buy these for souvenirs and with the money earned, she could buy shoes and perhaps a new dress. It was wonderful in the town, she told Nirmala. At the Smoke House Inn and hotels there were special trees lit up at night with flashing, twinkling lights and some had glittering decorations on them. It was like fairyland in the town. Special music was playing and anyone could stop and listen without paying money. People were smiling and

chatting and giving each other presents.

Nirmala stored all these delightful stories in her heart and imagined the beauty of the Christmas decorations. All year she dreamed about seeing the special sights and hearing the sound of bells and choirs as Madiah described them.

But Nirmala was growing weaker. One day she didn't even want to wake up, she was so exhausted. She said a sleepy goodbye to her worried mother in the morning and drifted off to sleep again. Her mother didn't go to pluck tea leaves that day. She anxiously called Madiah and old Jamal. Together, they propped Nirmala up in bed and persuaded her to sip some hot tea with sugar.

"Is there anything you want?" Madiah whispered, with her eyes full of tears.

"Yes," gasped Nirmala, "I want to see a Christmas tree, just once." Even whispering left her wheezing and struggling for air. Madiah ran home for her father. He gently lifted Nirmala and carried her like a baby against his strong chest.

"Where are we going?" she whispered weakly.

"To see your Christmas tree," replied the kind man, who had been like a father to her. Old Jamal slipped his gnarled hand into Madiah's firm young fingers and Nirmala's mother grabbed a woven mat. With Parum yapping at their heels, they set off.

They followed the muddy track which wound round behind the factory, past beds of sweet-smelling flowers and descended through rich black soil where vegetables grew. Villagers who were toiling in the terraced fields stopped their planting and watched the strange procession wending its way around the side of the hill.

Finally, they set her down on the woven mat her mother hurriedly unrolled, and Nirmala leaned back in her mother's arms, gazing at the most beautiful young fir tree. It was a deep spruce green and the tender young tips of each branch pointed heavenward like long, slender candles. The needles smelled of rich pine balsam.

Nirmala gazed in delight at her Christmas tree. She stretched out her frail hands to feel the twigs and needles and the sticky sap. As if they knew this was an important occasion, a host of gorgeous butterflies fluttered down from the skies and perched, quivering on the needles of the sapling. Their wings were like spangles of rich tinsel.

"No star," murmured Nirmala faintly. "They said Christmas trees always have a star." Madiah held back a branch so that her friend could see the top of the tree. There was a delicate spider web, woven in silver thread in the shape of a star. Dewdrops sparkled on the gossamer silk web, and the Christmas tree was perfect.

Nirmala's mother gently stroked her daughter's long dark hair. Contented, Nirmala watched the sun's rays light up her Christmas tree. On the hillside, with her dearest friends around her, she leaned back in her mother's arms and peacefully closed her eyes, drifting into the sleep of death. Her simple wish had been granted. She had seen her special Christmas tree.

A

1. What was wrong with Nirmala? How did this affect her appearance and her daily life?
2. Who kept her company while her mother and aunt were at work? What did she do all day?
3. How do we know that Nirmala came from a poor family? Give at least three reasons.
4. What was Nirmala's dying wish and how did it come true?

B

1. Were the plantation workers kind or selfish? Give reasons in support of your answer.

2. Do you know anyone who is an invalid or physically handicapped? How can you help such a person?
3. Was death frightening for Nirmala?
4. For whom do you feel more sorry — Nirmala, or her mother? Why?
5. If you were Madiah, how could you help Nirmala's mother after her daughter's death?

C

1. Write an imaginary dialogue between Nirmala and old Jamal, the blind man.
2. Compose a poem entitled "Death".

The Tin Grin Brigade

Jimmy was staying with his grandparents for the weekend. During the night he went to the bathroom to get a drink. On the shelf someone had left a glass of water and he was all set to take a swig when... Rattle, bump, clink. There was something in the glass! Cautiously Jimmy switched on the light — there was a set of false teeth grinning up at him from the glass! "How convenient," he thought once the shock had worn off. "I wish *my* teeth could be removed for cleaning."

Next morning, Grandpa asked what the commotion in the bathroom last night had been about. When Jimmy told him about his near miss, he laughed. "Grandma came from a poor family with many children," he explained. "They didn't go to the dentist, except to have bad teeth pulled out. But this caused problems when she grew up. Her teeth began to drift around her jaw, and lean into the holes where there was no tooth for support. Improper brushing caused infection and gum disease and by the time she was 50, she had to have all her teeth extracted," said Grandpa sadly. "Poor Gran; now she can only eat soft food, and her old gums are shrinking. I wish we'd known more about dental care in our youth."

Several days later, Jimmy was playing soccer at school. He made a dive in the mud to save a goal just as another player went to kick the ball. Poor Jimmy felt a hard boot smash into his mouth. His lip bled, and his front teeth felt loose and sore. The referee sent him off the field, and his mother took him straight to the dentist.

After tapping the loose teeth, the dentist took some X-rays which showed the long roots of Jimmy's teeth. "Look at those prominent front teeth, Jim," said the dentist. "They have been loosened by this accident, and you'll need braces to straighten them. I'll introduce you to Dr Huang, an orthodontist, and he will design a brace for your teeth to help move them into their correct place. I'll arrange for you to see him before school tomorrow.''

Next morning Jimmy sat nervously in a big green chair in Dr Huang's clinic. It didn't look like a dental clinic; it looked like a mechanic's workshop. Dr Huang came in smiling, and explained, ''I've had a look at your X-rays, and I'm confident that if we fit you with a brace now, we'll gradually be able to move your teeth into a better position. You are going to have a great grin one day.''

Jimmy wished he felt as confident as the dentist sounded, but being too polite to disagree, just nodded. Then Dr Huang explained the whole process to Jimmy; how he'd make a model of Jimmy's teeth; how the wire braces would be made and fitted and why the dental work would take such a long time. ''At each of your monthly visits I'll adjust your braces, and take some more X-rays. From the X-rays you'll be able to see that the position of your teeth really is changing; that should help keep you from getting discouraged.''

On Jimmy's next visit to Dr Huang's, his brace was fitted. It looked very ugly and made his jaws ache. Before leaving the clinic, Dr Huang gave him advice on how to care for his teeth and his new braces. ''You must be careful to brush your teeth properly and rinse your braces after eating. Try to avoid sticky or hard foods and chew everything carefully.

''At first your teeth will be a bit sore, but that means that the braces are doing their job properly. And remember; wherever you go, your braces must go too. If you have to remove them, put them carefully in a clean plastic container. They're quite fragile, and easily lost.

''Don't worry if your speech is slurred. One of my patients says he feels as if his mouth is full of marbles! And if the wires rub your gums, I've some wax which will take care of that for you.

"You'll soon get used to them and in the end, it really will be worth it. I promise you."

Arriving home, the first hurdle to be faced was dinner. How was he ever going to eat with a mouthful of wire? But his mum had already thought of that. She remembered how, when Anna (Jimmy's sister) had first got braces, she'd only been able to take liquids and soft foods, so she prepared Jimmy's favourite soup and gave him a big serving of chocolate-fudge icecream for desert.

Anna tried to cheer him up. "Don't look so glum, Jim," she said. "You'll hardly notice them after a while. I don't. I know they're uncomfortable now and that they don't look all that nice, but it's better than having no teeth. This way they'll look better than ever by the time the treatment's complete."

"I know," said Jimmy. "It's just that I don't want to be different from my friends. They're sure to make fun of me."

"Is that all?" laughed Anna. "Then why don't you make friends with other kids who have braces? There are probably quite a few in your school and I'm sure Dr Huang can give you the names of some of his patients. You could even start a club; only people who wear braces can join!"

Jimmy thought that was a great idea. If he knew other kids with braces he wouldn't feel out of place. He mentioned his idea to Dr Huang at his next visit and he offered to let Jimmy hold the first meeting of his club in the clinic's waiting room. "It's a pity I can't join," he said laughingly. "Perhaps you'd let me be an adviser to your Tin Grin Brigade."

The following week, more than a dozen children crammed into Dr Huang's waiting room, curious to know just what the Tin Grin Brigade was all about. "First, let's introduce ourselves," said Jimmy. "I'm Tinsel Teeth," piped up one little girl. "They call me Cheese Please," said the plump boy next to her, and some of the children started chuckling. "My Grandpa nicknamed me Sore Jaw," offered a sulky boy. "So

I call him Grumpa, because he's always grumbling." They all laughed at each other's names and somehow they didn't seem so bad. The children told of how they felt when others made fun of them because of their braces. They all agreed that being able to share their experiences made them feel better; more confident. They shared advice on how to look after their braces and Dr Huang was on hand to answer all their questions. The Tin Grin Brigade was a great success.

More and more brace-faced kids joined them and when any of them came to the end of their treatment, they'd have a farewell party to celebrate. Jimmy learned to laugh with his friends when they thought up even more ingenious nicknames and when his braces pinched and hurt, he'd remind himself of poor Grandma and her false teeth. He knew that even if it did take a long time, one day his teeth would be straight and strong. Some things, he decided, were worth waiting for.

A

1. How did Jimmy's grandmother come to lose all her teeth?
2. Name some of the problems which Jimmy could expect to face once he had his braces fitted.
3. Why do you think they called the club the Tin Grin Brigade?
4. What were some of the nicknames?
5. Why did Jimmy not want to wear braces, even though he knew it was for his own good?

B

1. Jimmy needed braces to straighten his teeth. Can you think of any other special appliances which people sometimes have to use?
2. The Tin Grin Brigade was a self-help group. Do you know of any real self-help groups in Singapore?
3. Do you think it's unkind to call people by nicknames?

C

1. Write an imaginary account of Jimmy's first day at school with braces.
2. Perhaps you've had to visit a dentist or even an orthodontist. Give an account of your experience.
3. Write a short essay on the theme 'Some things are worth waiting for'.

Bobby's Boots

Bobby was very depressed. He did not want to eat, and he could not sleep. A serious accident had left him badly injured and the doctors said he would never play sport again, and would probably have a permanent limp. Bobby often thought about the accident. He had tripped over his shoelace whilst crossing the highway, and a motorcycle had rammed into him. He remembered the noise, the speeding ambulance and the pain. Even after a long and complicated operation, the doctors were not optimistic since it looked very much as if the nerves in both legs had been crushed.

Bobby's family came to visit him every day. His brother brought him games and puzzles, but he didn't want to play; his sister brought him books, but he didn't feel like reading; his mother brought his favourite food, but Bobby didn't feel hungry. He had lost interest in everything.

One day his favourite teacher, Mr Lin, visited him. Mr Lin was Bobby's form master and his football coach. Bobby liked him and felt flattered that he had taken the time to visit him. As Mr Lin was about to leave, he handed Bobby a box, and said, "I expect you to be captain of the team next season, so you had better start making those legs work again."

When he left, Bobby opened the box. Inside was a football jersey in his school colours, and a pair of brand new football boots. Bobby's mother wept when she saw the present. "How thoughtless and insensitive," she cried. But Bobby thought a lot about the present, and fell asleep clutching the navy jersey, and dreaming about playing football again.

Next day, he asked his brother, "Tom, can you please bring me some black shoe polish next time you come — and a brush too?"

When visiting hours were over and everyone had gone home,

Bobby threw back the blanket and looked at his numb legs. He leaned over and grasping his pyjama legs, began pulling first one leg up and down and then the other. Just then Dr Wu came in.

"Good for you, Bob. It's time we started physiotherapy to keep your muscles from wasting away. Be ready at 8 a.m. I'll send a wheelchair down to fetch you."

Bobby gulped down his breakfast next morning, he was impatient to get started. He refused to let the orderly lift him into the wheelchair. "Let me just lean on you," insisted Bobby, slowly pulling one leg after the other. He wriggled to the edge of the bed and crash-landed in the wheelchair flushed with victory. It was his first real achievement in the long months since his accident.

Over the next few weeks, Bobby worked really hard. Every morning he wheeled his way to the gym. Before his accident, Bobby had been very fit and energetic, but now every little movement took so much effort. Sometimes, Bobby felt like giving up. Then he would look at his football boots and remember his coach saying, "Get well, Bobby. We need you to be captain of the school football team next season."

Bobby was also studying hard. It was not easy to keep up with his lessons without regular tuition. But his teachers set assignments, and his friends came every few days bringing new work and taking his completed work back to the teachers for marking. It was a long hard struggle, but Bobby persevered. He was determined to succeed.

How Bobby worked! Every day he pulled bars and lifted weights. The nurses massaged and manipulated his legs, and the orderly taught him how to use crutches.

Every night, no matter how tired, Bobby polished his boots, saying over and over again, "I will be wearing these soon. I'm going to be captain of the team." When his classmates visited him, they kept him up to date with the team's progress, giving him all the news and gossip. Dad brought him the newspaper every day, and they cut out football stories from the sports' page. Sometimes at night, for a treat, the night nurse would allow him to walk with his crutches and leg irons along to another room where a frail old man had a television set. Together they watched matches and discussed ball games. The old man had once represented his state, and Bobby loved to hear stories from his football days.

On his birthday, Bobby woke up feeling rather sorry for himself. "It isn't much fun spending your birthday in hospital," he grumbled.

"Just you wait and see," smiled the nurse knowingly. In the afternoon, during visiting hours, his whole family arrived, bearing a big birthday cake and lots of snacks. They had a wonderful party, right there in the ward, with his room mates and the nurses joining in. It was really a lovely surprise.

That evening, the whole of the School Team crowded into his room, dressed in their football gear. Even their coach had come. "We want to take a photo for the school magazine," Mr Lin explained. "So you had better put your uniform on and comb your hair."

What excitement! Bobby struggled into his Number 1 jersey (he had tried it on several times at night when the others were sleeping), and he took his boots out of their box. Suddenly a look of disappointment clouded his face.

"I have no socks, Sir," he mumbled.

"Oh yes you have," said Tom who was also in the team. "Happy birthday, Bob. I thought you'd like these." Tom pulled a parcel from his backpack, and Bobby opened it to find heavy navy socks with two white stripes. Just like the rest of the team.

"Here, let's get these on," said Mr Lin gruffly. He fumbled around, pulling the socks on over Bobby's skinny, white legs in their ugly iron braces. The socks went right up to Bobby's knees, completely covering the braces. "There," he said finally. "Now for the boots." And for the very first time those highly polished and much-loved boots were on his feet.

"How's that?" asked Tom.

"They feel tight," replied Bobby. "My feet must have grown."

"They *feel*? You can really *feel* them?" asked Mr Lin in surprise.

"Yes, they press the iron against my anklebone. It hurts," said Bobby. Suddenly everyone was talking at once. Dr Wu popped into see what all the fuss was about.

"His boots hurt. He can feel!" said Tom overwhelmed. Dr Wu pressed and poked, he twisted and bent Bobby's legs, while all his team mates and ward friends watched, fascinated.

"Your nerves are healing, Bob. Your perseverance has paid off. You *WILL* walk again. What a marvellous birthday surprise, boy."

"I knew I would walk again! Soon I will run and jump too. I'm going to be Captain of the football team."

Bobby pulled his legs over the side of the bed and plopped into his wheelchair. He rolled along the corridor with all the boys behind him. "Like the Pied Piper, aren't you," teased the duty nurse. They stopped in front of the Orthopaedic Department, and Mr Lin arranged the players in rows for their photograph. Bobby's wheelchair was in the middle of the front row. "You're our centre-forward, Bob," said Tom proudly. "There's only one thing missing," remarked Dr Wu, as he tossed something to Bob. "I think you need a ball. Happy birthday, Bobby. The nurses and physiotherapist and all your room-mates would like you to have this. You have impressed us all with your positive attitude and courage." It was a brand new football, signed by all his friends. Bobby was very touched. "Now we're all set, can we please take the photo, boys?" asked Mr Lin. "Please, Sir," said Bobby

shyly, "will you come in the photo with us? Dr Wu takes X-rays, so he can easily handle your camera." Beaming with delight, Mr Lin knelt in front of the team, disguising Bob's wheelchair.

When it was developed, it was a beautiful photo. Bobby had a copy hanging above his bed in the hospital, and the football was in his bedside locker. The boots, tied by their laces, were slung over the end of his bed. They encouraged Bobby while he worked at strengthening his muscles, as did the support of his family and friends. It was a long, uphill struggle, but Bobby did recover. That season he was assistant coach and cheerleader for his team. He would sit on the sidelines, wearing his football strip, and support his team at every practice — except, of course, when he had to go back into hospital for further treatment.

Two seasons later, Bobby was out on the field — in bigger boots. The boys teased him that he had grown too big for his boots, and so he had! His muscles were stronger now, and his legs looked more sturdy, despite the long purple scars from the surgery.

Today, Bobby still has a well-polished pair of unused boots in his cupboard, and on his desk there is a photo of the best team in the world.

A
1. How did Bobby lose the use of his legs?
2. What gave Bobby the incentive to recover the use of his legs?
3. In what way did his family and friends help him when he was in hospital?
4. How did Bobby celebrate his birthday in hospital?

B
1. What was the turning point in Bobby's recovery? Describe how a positive attitude can help you overcome problems.

2. How could you help a friend in Bobby's position?
3. Bobby had his family and friends for support. Where else might a handicapped person be able to get help and support?
4. What special problems might Bobby have had if he was unable to walk?

C
1. Imagine you have a friend like Bobby. In a short essay, describe your plan for helping him get back on his feet.
2. For a moment, imagine that Bobby did not regain the use of his legs, and that you have to take care of him. Describe a normal day's activities.

Homecoming

CD was so excited! For weeks he'd talked of nothing else. His beloved son was coming home to Johor after four long years studying in Britain. CD had traded in his precious motorbike and his wife had pawned her jewellery to provide funds for their only son's expensive education.

Ed had written occasionally complaining about the cold weather and the unfamiliar food. He didn't like living in a hostel where he had to wash his own clothes, and he hated commuting by train. Most of Ed's letters were requests for more money.

But all those lean years were behind them now, CD mused. Ed had passed his subjects and gained a BSc degree. His proud parents could not afford to go to the graduation ceremony, but pleaded with Ed for a photo of the grand occasion. There he was, wearing a strange gown and hat, and clutching the precious diploma in both hands. It was a serious, unsmiling photo, not the victorious grin his father wore as he proudly showed the picture to all his village friends.

Mama had been pounding *sambal* and grinding spices for days. She had slaved over an open fire preparing all Ed's favourite dishes. Ah, he would really enjoy coming home to the house where he was born. Her daughter, Lucy, never complained about Ed being the favourite child; she accepted that the only son would be given every opportunity to succeed. Lucy was also eagerly awaiting Ed's return, for she would bask in the reflected glory of her brother, the graduate. Only two others from their village had ever been to university; one of them had never returned.

Lucy and her mother had sewn new curtains for the rough timbered room that was Ed's old bedroom. They polished the wood and painted an old desk. They put a potted plant in the corner and even bought a fan because Ed might feel uncomfortable in the steamy heat of the day.

The great day finally arrived, and by 7 a.m. the little family was waiting at the railway station. Mother had packed food for the trip so they would not need to get off the train. All the way to Kuala Lumpur they chattered excitedly about the highlight of their lives: Ed's homecoming.

Hours before the plane landed, Ed's family was at Subang Airport. Dad was nervously tugging his hair to cover the bald spots. His wife had disguised her worn out body under a bright new *sarung*. Only her work-stained hands and rough feet betrayed her hard life and tough work. She tended to smile with her lips closed these days, so people wouldn't notice the gaping holes where several decayed teeth had been removed. Dad wished he could afford dental treatment for her, but she had insisted that Ed's education was more important.

"Announcing the arrival of Flight 101 from London. Passengers now disembarking at Gate 4," boomed a voice over the sound system. Clutching at the railing, CD, his wife and Lucy peered anxiously into the busy arrival hall. Afraid of missing Ed, they craned their necks to catch a glimpse of their golden boy.

"There he is!" squealed Lucy in excitement, pointing at a long-haired young man striding through the Customs barrier.

"Why, he's so tall now," murmured her mother, not realising she had shrunk with bending low under many burdens.

The tall stranger stared at them in disbelief. Ash dropped from the cigarette he held in his soft hand. Shiny cufflinks flashed on his shirt sleeves. His glasses fogged up as he left the airconditioned lounge. The musky scent from his aftershave lotion wafted towards their eager faces.

Ed stood rooted to the spot for a long time before stretching out his hand awkwardly towards them, mumbling with embarrassment at their enthusiastic welcome. "Pa, Ma, Sis, I didn't expect to see you here. You shouldn't have come." He ran his fingers through his long hair in a gesture of frustration, glancing furtively around to see if people were watching. He sighed with resignation. An attractive and elegantly dressed young lady trundled her luggage up beside him saying, "Guess what, Eddie? I managed to sneak 3 bottles of brandy past that silly old customs officer..." Her voice trailed off as her eyes focussed on the dishevelled looking family.

"Er, Sarah, I'd like you to meet my relatives. They've come from Johor," mumbled Ed. "Sarah was my classmate in England."

"Nice to meet you," said Sarah coldly, glancing at their poor clothing and noting that the old woman still clutched a plastic bag of leftover food in her hand.

"Ed is ashamed of us," thought CD with a sickening realisation. "Ashamed of us, his family. These flashy, dressy people are his life now. We've lost our son." The uncomfortable silence was broken by Ed, who suggested in a falsely light-hearted voice, "Sarah, why don't you go and queue for a taxi. I'll join you in a minute."

Sarah's adoring smile at Ed vanished as her gaze moved over the family. She nodded curtly, then minced away in her fashionable high heels, skilfully manoeuvering the luggage trolley.

"Ma, Pa, Sis — it wasn't necessary to come," said Ed sheepishly. "I suppose you took the day off work, Pa?" CD nodded, and Lucy chipped in, "I took two days off school to welcome you home, Ko." She felt confused and betrayed by her hero.

"Nothing would keep us away, son," said Mother, her eyes filling with tears. Could this cold, unapproachable man be the child she had cherished all his growing years? Why could he not welcome his family with the warmth he showed that superficial glamour-girl? What did *she* have to offer him? Surely she couldn't adore him the way they, his doting family did.

"I've arranged to stay with Sarah's family for a few days, Pa," Ed mumbled, averting his eyes from their puzzled, pained expressions. He could no longer look them straight in the eye. "Why don't you go on home, and I'll come down to Johor Baru at the weekend. I've got some friends to look up here, and of course I must find a job."

"Your room is ready," blurted Lucy, grabbing his arms and gazing up at him. "I've prepared your favourite *sambal tumis* and *kueh lapis*," whispered his mother, her sad eyes spilling hot tears down her wrinkled old cheeks. "Everyone in the village is planning a welcome home party for you tomorrow, son," said Pa in a barely audible voice. "We are all so proud of you."

"Look, Pa," said Ed awkwardly. "Sure, I appreciate you giving me the chance to study abroad, and I didn't disappoint you. I passed all my exams. But I'm different now — after four years of academic life, I'm no longer the shy *kampung* kid who only knew how to catch fish and pick coconuts. My life will be here in the city. I'll get a good office job, then I'm going to marry Sarah."

His parents were too shocked and disappointed to reply. Ed glanced at the taxi rank. "Oh — she's loading her luggage into a taxi," he said. "I've got to go. Don't be sad — it's just that I've grown up. See you at the weekend." And with an awkward hug for each of them, Ed walked quickly away from his past security into a falsely glittering future.

A
1. Why were Ed's parents so proud of him?
2. What sacrifices had the family made so that Ed could study overseas?

3. What preparations had the family made for Ed's homecoming?
4. Describe the meeting at the airport. What was Ed's reaction when he saw his family waiting for him?
5. How had Ed changed in four years?

B
1. Do you feel sorry for Ed or his parents? Why?
2. Do you think Ed's family should have gone to the airport to meet him?
3. How do you think Ed's family explained his delayed arrival to the rest of the village?
4. Have you ever been embarrassed by a member of your family? How? Whose fault was it — yours or theirs?

C
1. Write an imaginary discussion between Ed and Sarah in the taxi.
2. Perhaps someone in your family has gone overseas to study. What changes, if any, did you notice in them when they returned?

Other Books for Secondary 1 and 2

Moral Education
THEY LIVED FOR OTHERS, Rosemary Pearson Chen (GB S'pore)

English Readers
MOWGLI STORIES BOOKS 1-3, Rudyard Kipling (GB S'pore)
ANIMAL STORIES, Rudyard Kipling (GB S'pore)
A TASTE FOR BOOKS Books 1-3, Thompson & Garnett (H.M. UK)
CARRY ON READING, RED BOOKS 1-6, BLUE BOOKS 1-6,
  Thompson (S&S UK)

English Language
FOUNDATION SKILLS, BOOKS 1-2, Barber & Thomson (Letts UK)
ENGLISH SKILLS, BOOKS 1-6, Burgess (S&S UK)
ENGLISH IS EASY, BOOKS 1-4, Hossack (Lutterworth UK)
CHECK POINTS: BASIC SKILLS FOR LITERACY, Chatfield (B&H UK)
ESSENTIALS OF ENGLISH, BOOKS 1-3 (H.M. UK)
READ AND RESPOND, Tarbitt (H.M. UK)

Mathematics
CAMBRIDGE MATHEMATICS, BOOKS 1-2, Marsden (GB S'pore)
  June 1987
GRADED EXAMPLES IN MATHS, BOOKS 1-8, Heylings (S&S UK)

Music
FORTY PLUS TEN (SONGS FOR SCHOOLS), Maxwell-Timmins
  (S&S UK)
NEW-WAY SONG BOOK, MacMahon (S&S UK)
MAKE MUSIC FUN, BOOKS 1-4, Maxwell-Timmins (S&S UK)